BEADY EYE

Different Gear

STILL SPEEDING

&

WISE PUBLICATIONS
part of The Music Sales Group
London/New York/Paris/Sydney/Copenhagen/Berlin/Madrid/Hong Kong/Tokyo

PUBLISHED BY
WISE PUBLICATIONS
14-15 BERNERS STREET, LONDON W1T 3LJ, UK.

EXCLUSIVE DISTRIBUTORS:
MUSIC SALES LIMITED
DISTRIBUTION CENTRE, NEWMARKET ROAD,
BURY ST EDMUNDS, SUFFOLK IP33 3YB, UK.
MUSIC SALES PTY LIMITED
20 RESOLUTION DRIVE, CARINGBAH,
NSW 2229, AUSTRALIA.

ORDER NO. AM1003090
ISBN: 978-1-78038-012-4
THIS BOOK © COPYRIGHT 2011 WISE PUBLICATIONS,
A DIVISION OF MUSIC SALES LIMITED.

EDITED BY ADRIAN HOPKINS.
MUSIC ARRANGED BY MATT COWE.
MUSIC PROCESSED BY PAUL EWERS MUSIC DESIGN.
PRINTED IN THE EU.

YOUR GUARANTEE OF QUALITY:

AS PUBLISHERS, WE STRIVE TO PRODUCE EVERY BOOK
TO THE HIGHEST COMMERCIAL STANDARDS.

THIS BOOK HAS BEEN CAREFULLY DESIGNED TO MINIMISE AWKWARD PAGE
TURNS AND TO MAKE PLAYING FROM IT A REAL PLEASURE.

PARTICULAR CARE HAS BEEN GIVEN TO SPECIFYING ACID-FREE, NEUTRAL-SIZED PAPER
MADE FROM PULPS WHICH HAVE NOT BEEN ELEMENTAL CHLORINE BLEACHED.
THIS PULP IS FROM FARMED SUSTAINABLE FORESTS AND WAS PRODUCED
WITH SPECIAL REGARD FOR THE ENVIRONMENT.

THROUGHOUT, THE PRINTING AND BINDING HAVE BEEN PLANNED TO ENSURE A STURDY,
ATTRACTIVE PUBLICATION WHICH SHOULD GIVE YEARS OF ENJOYMENT.

IF YOUR COPY FAILS TO MEET OUR HIGH STANDARDS, PLEASE INFORM US
AND WE WILL GLADLY REPLACE IT.

WWW.MUSICSALES.COM

FOUR LETTER WORD 4

MILLIONAIRE 11

THE ROLLER 20

BEATLES AND STONES 26

WIND UP DREAM 35

BRING THE LIGHT 43

FOR ANYONE 49

KILL FOR A DREAM 52

Standing On The Edge Of The Noise 57

WIGWAM 64

THREE RING CIRCUS 71

THE BEAT GOES ON 76

THE MORNING SON 80

Guitar Tablature Explained 86

FOUR LETTER WORD

Words & Music by Liam Gallagher, Gem Archer & Andy Bell

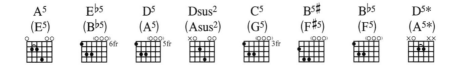

Intro

†Symbols in parentheses represent names with respect to capoed guitar.
Symbols above represent actual sounding chords. Tab 0 = Capo 5th fret.
*Gtr. 2 power chord shapes played with open top three strings *ad lib.*
Chord symbols denote simplified chord names.

w/fast wah ⌐┤

Gtr. 3 cont. in slashes

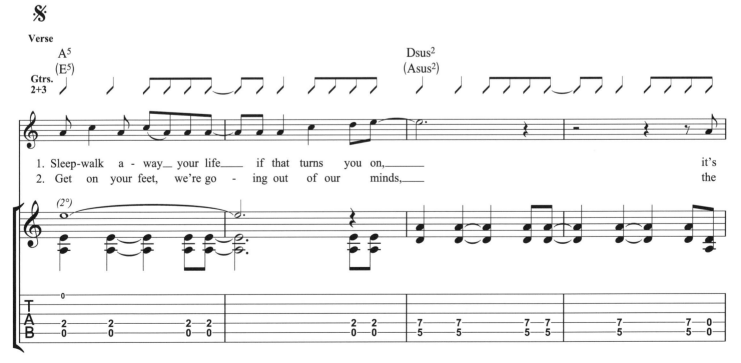

Verse

Gtrs. 2+3

1. Sleep-walk a - way___ your life____ if that turns you on,_____ it's
2. Get on your feet, we're go - ing out of our minds,_____ the

5

all in a mo - ment, look a - way__ and it's gone.__
wheels need to roll, the clock on the wall__ says it's time.__

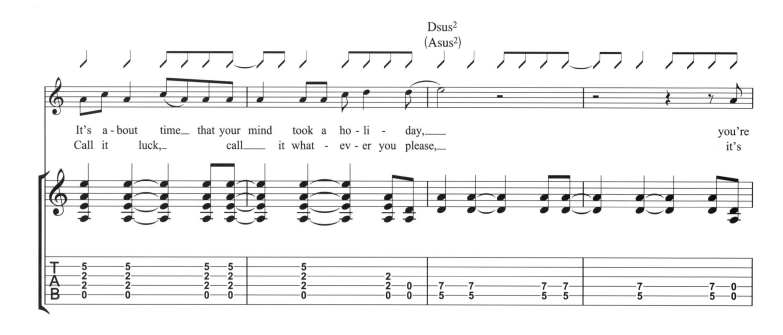

It's a - bout time__ that your mind took a ho - li - day,__ you're
Call it luck,__ call__ it what - ev - er you please,__ it's

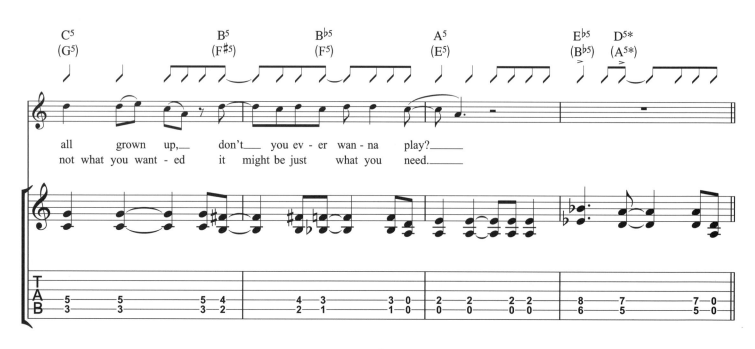

all grown up,__ don't you ev - er wan - na play?__
not what you want - ed it might be just what you need.__

MILLIONAIRE

Words & Music by Liam Gallagher, Gem Archer & Andy Bell

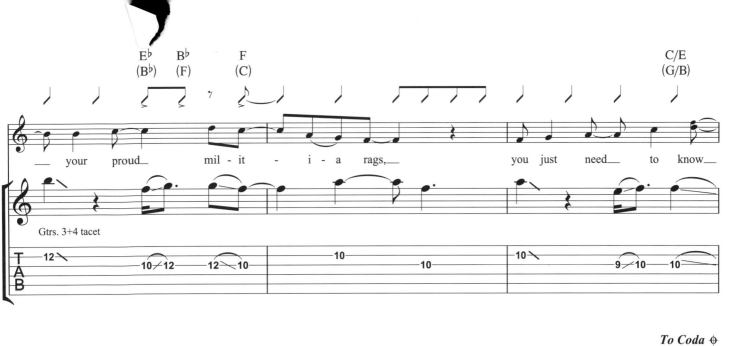

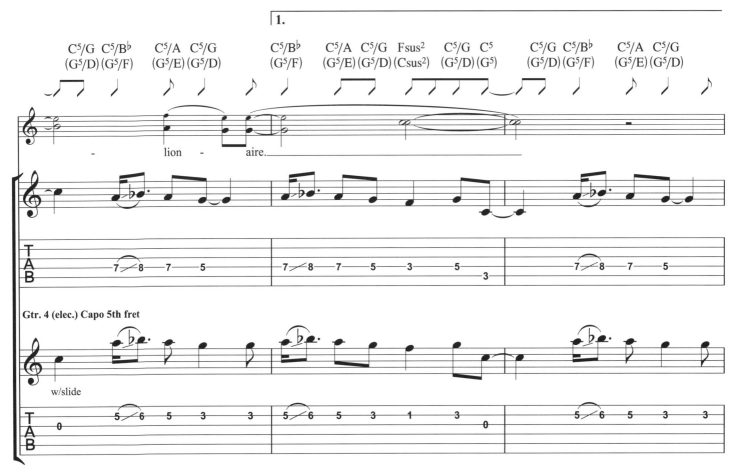

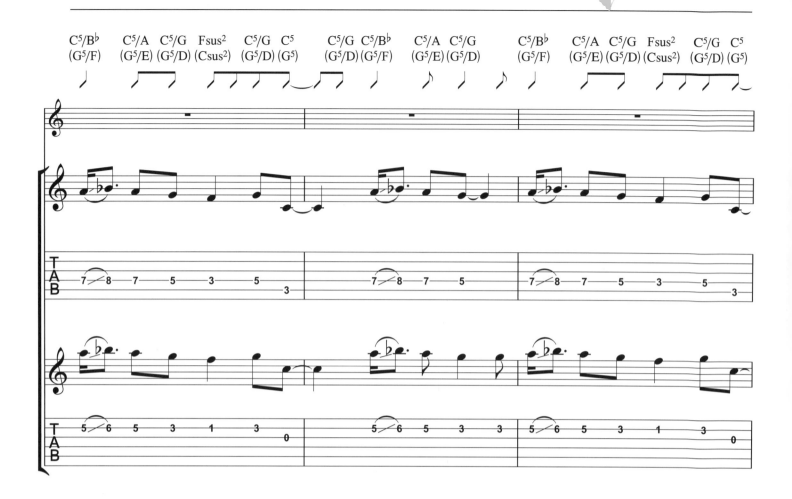

Like a mil - lion - aire._

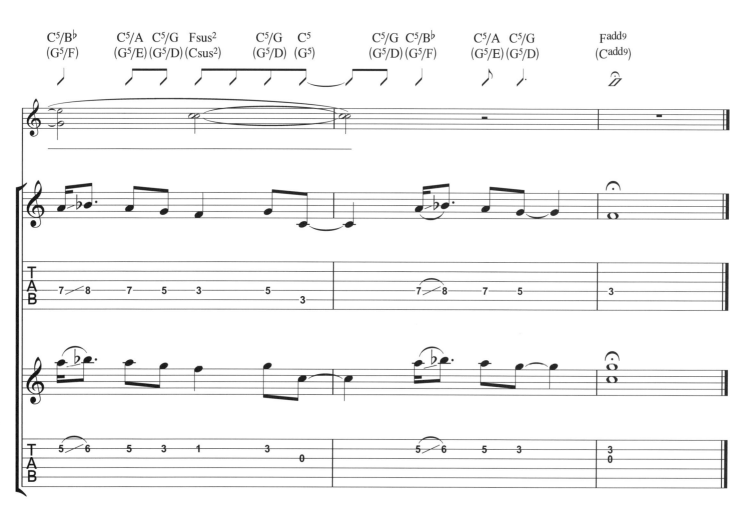

THE ROLLER

Words & Music by Liam Gallagher, Gem Archer & Andy Bell

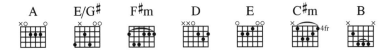

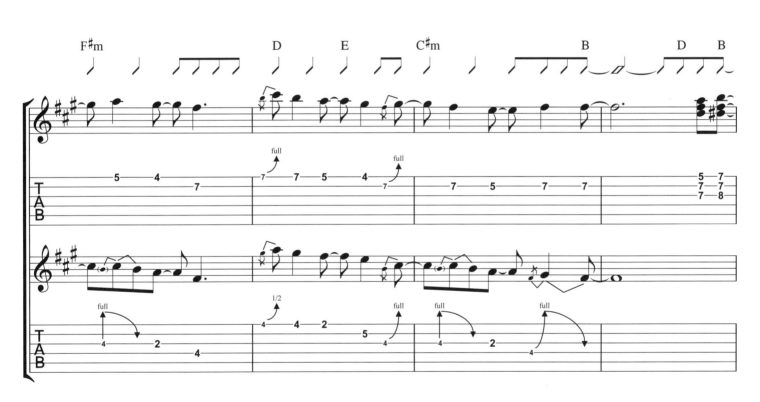

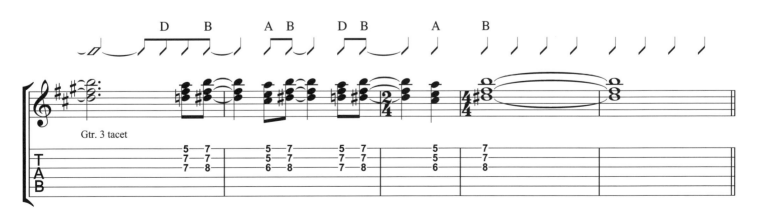

23

BEATLES AND STONES

Words & Music by Liam Gallagher, Gem Archer & Andy Bell

†Symbols in parentheses represent names with respect to capoed guitar.
Symbols above represent actual sounding chords. Tab 0 = Capo 1st fret.

I'm gon - na stand the test_ of time_ like Bea - tles and Stones._
I'm gon - na stand the test_ of time_ like Bea - tles and Stones._

2. Well it

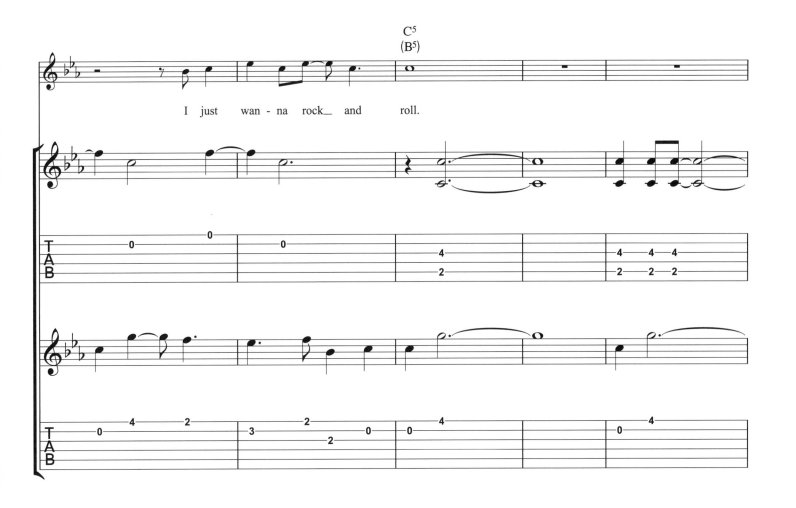

I just wan - na rock__ and roll.

I'm gon - na stand the test__ of time__ like

Get out___ the way.___

WIND UP DREAM

Words & Music by Liam Gallagher, Gem Archer & Andy Bell

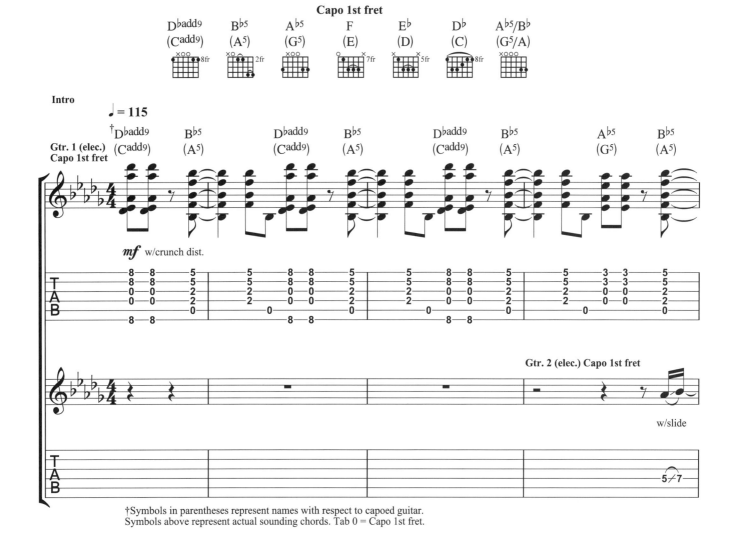

†Symbols in parentheses represent names with respect to capoed guitar.
Symbols above represent actual sounding chords. Tab 0 = Capo 1st fret.

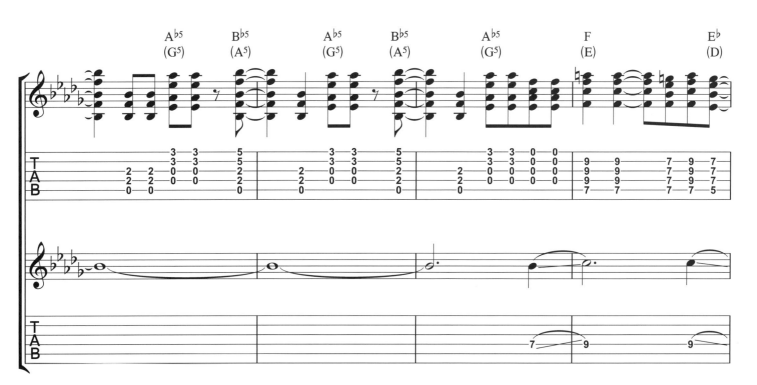

36

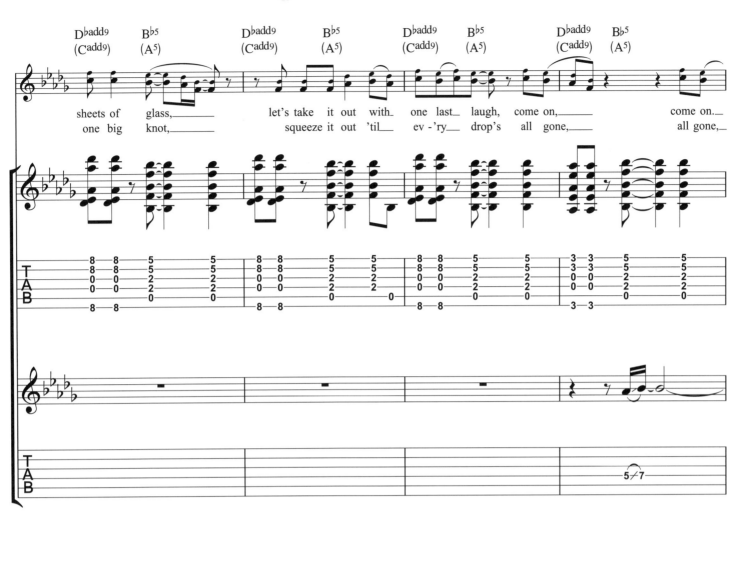

sheets of glass, let's take it out with one last laugh, come on, come on.
one big knot, squeeze it out 'til ev-'ry drop's all gone, all gone,

come on.

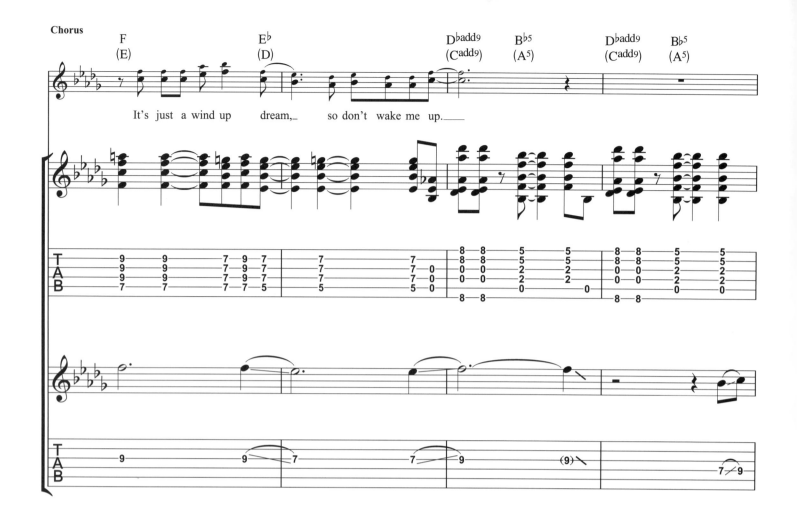

Chorus

It's just a wind up dream,— so don't wake me up.—

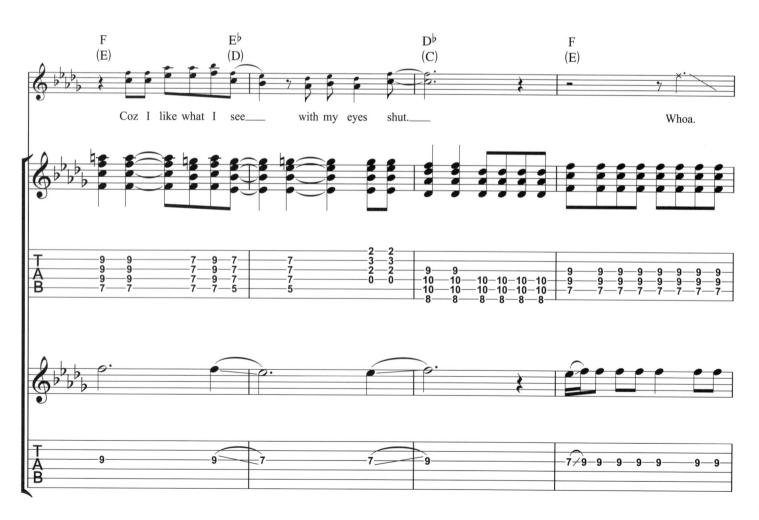

Coz I like what I see—— with my eyes shut.—— Whoa.

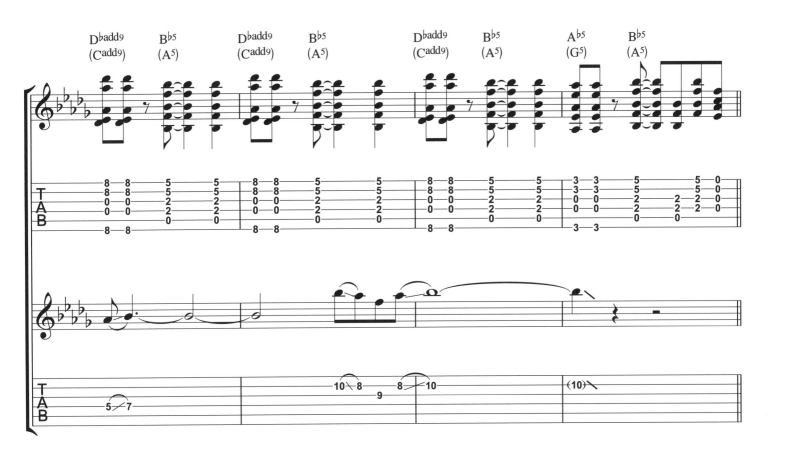

Verse

3. So - lid gold glint in your eye,_____ a cheek - y grin that real - ly

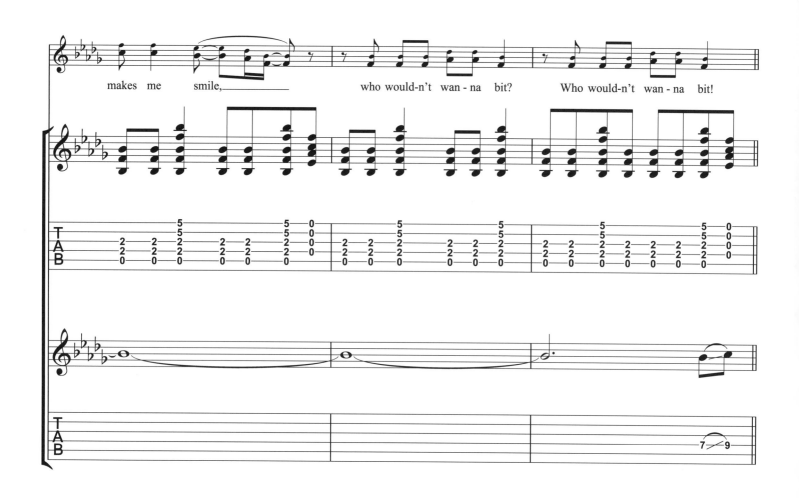

makes me smile,_____ who would-n't wan - na bit? Who would-n't wan - na bit!

Chorus

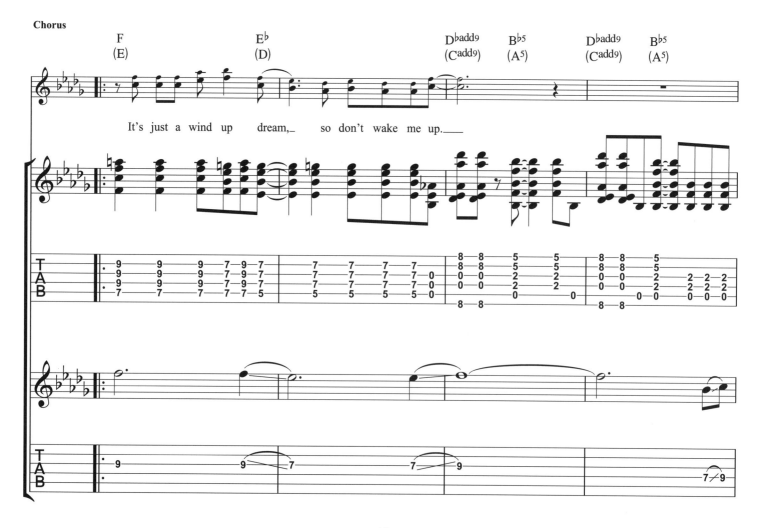

It's just a wind up dream,_ so don't wake me up._

BRING THE LIGHT

Words & Music by Liam Gallagher, Gem Archer & Andy Bell

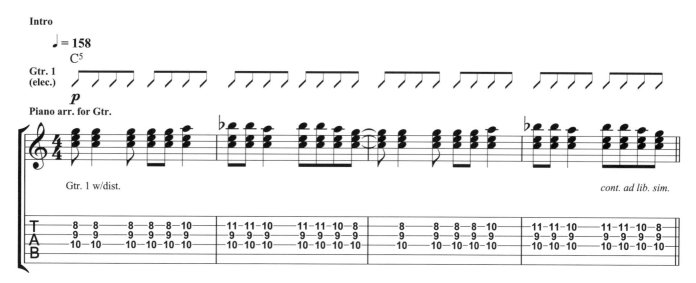

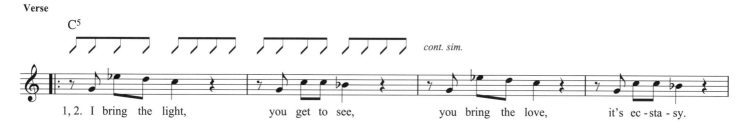

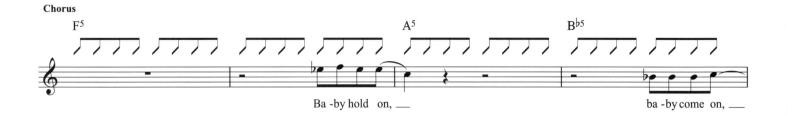

Ba -by hold on, ___ ba -by come on, ___

ba -by come on, ___ you're get -ting off, get -ting off.

Ba - by hold on, _____ ba - by come on, ___

___ ba - by come on, ___ you're get -ting off, get -ting off.

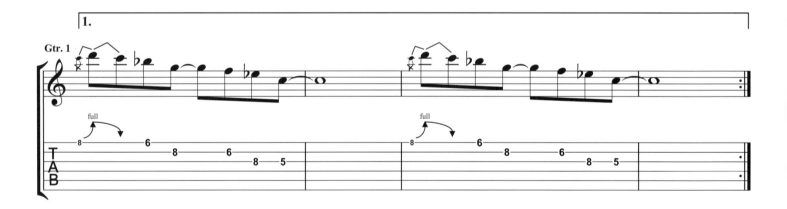

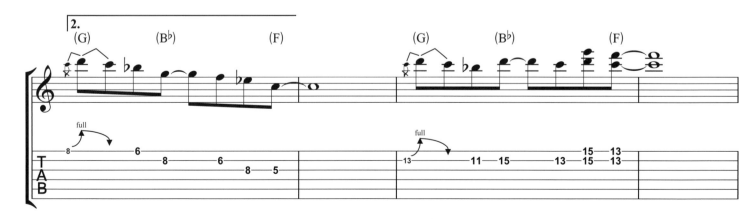

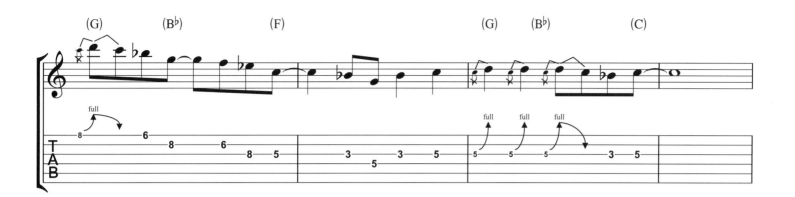

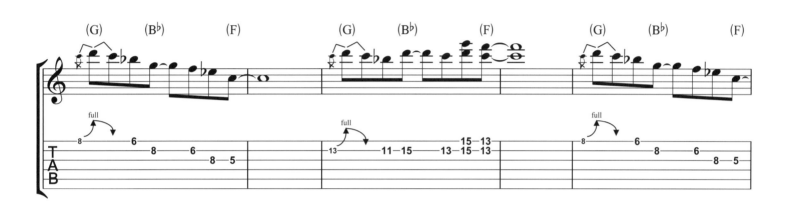

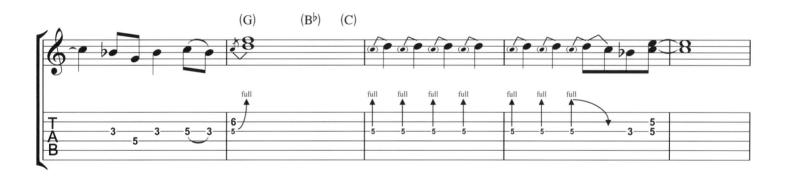

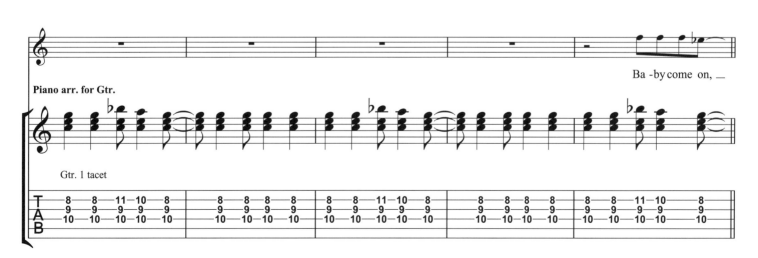

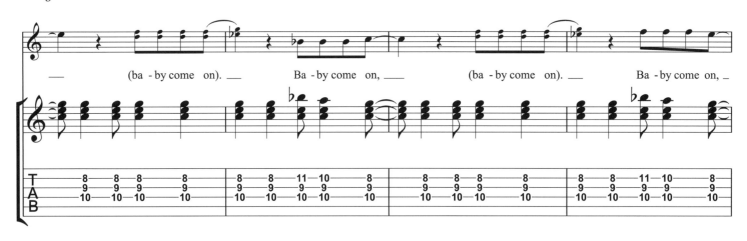

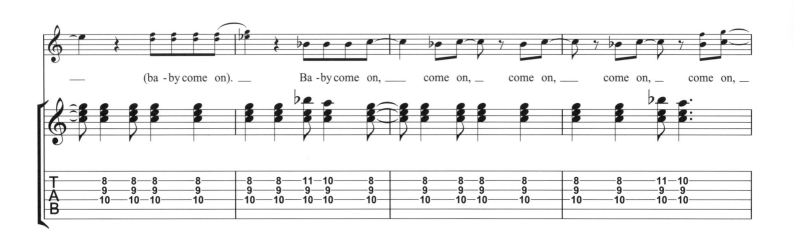

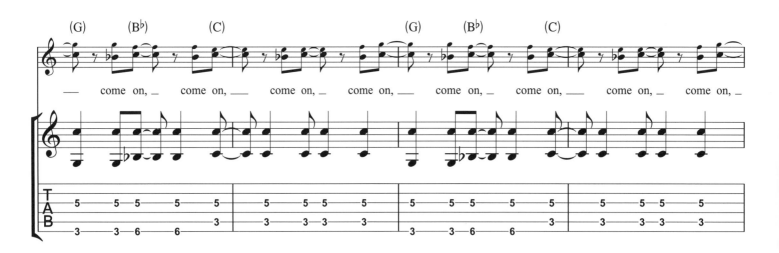

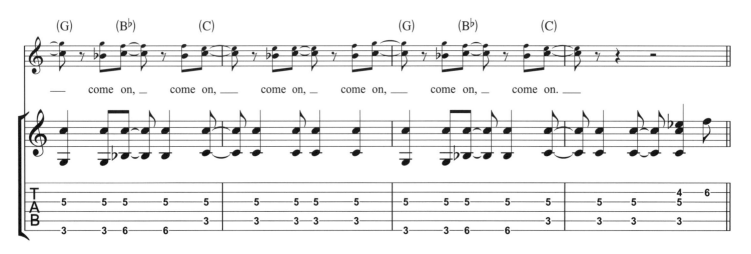

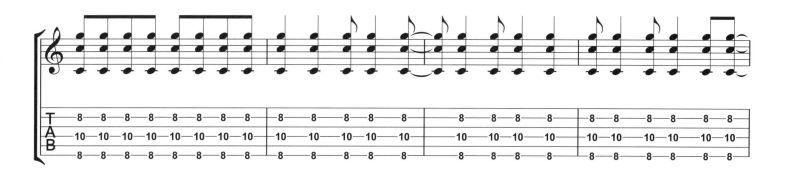

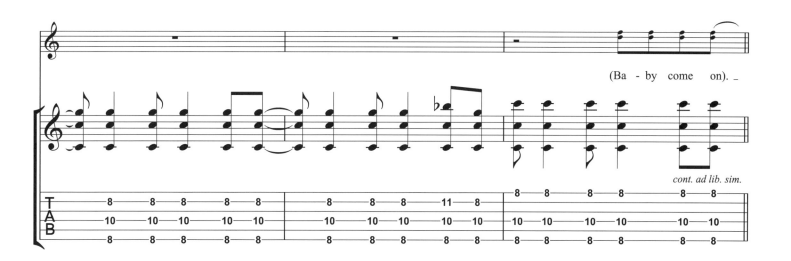

(Ba - by come on). _

cont. ad lib. sim.

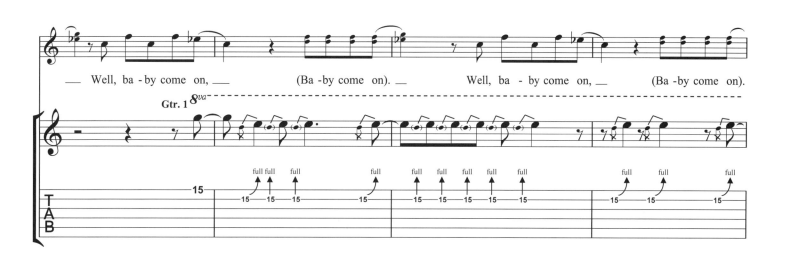

_ Well, ba - by come on, ___ (Ba -by come on). _ Well, ba - by come on, ___ (Ba -by come on).

Gtr. 1 *8va*

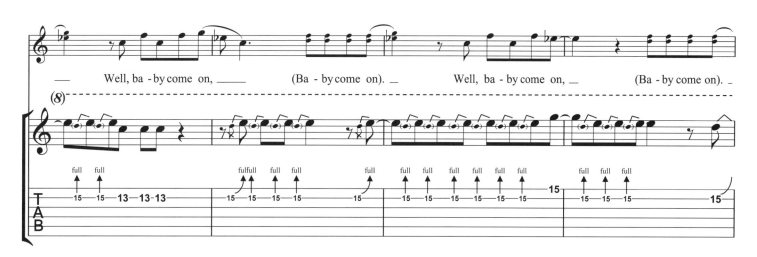

_ Well, ba - by come on, _____ (Ba - by come on). _ Well, ba - by come on, _ (Ba -by come on). _

(8)

FOR ANYONE

Words & Music by Liam Gallagher, Gem Archer & Andy Bell

50

51

KILL FOR A DREAM

Words & Music by Liam Gallagher, Gem Archer & Andy Bell

Pre-chorus

Na, na, na, na, na. Na, na, na, na, na. Na, na, na, na, na.

Outro

Gtr. 5 (elec. 12 str.)

p grad. cresc.

Standing On The Edge Of The Noise

Words & Music by Liam Gallagher, Gem Archer & Andy Bell

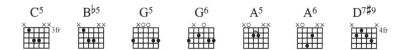

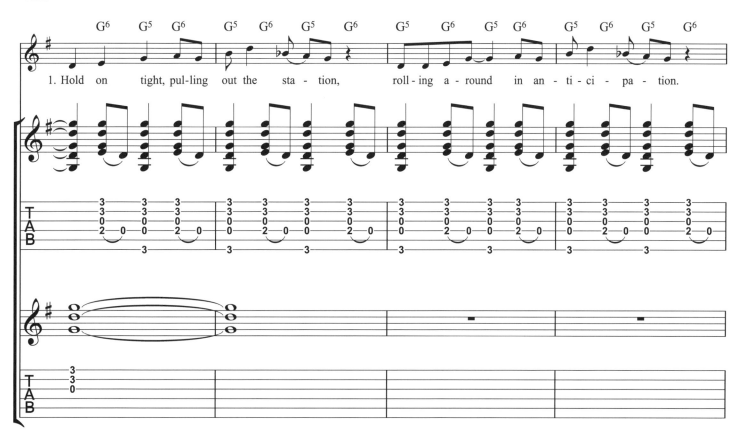

Said our good-byes__ to__ ev-'ry-thing   and we're there.__

2. Your

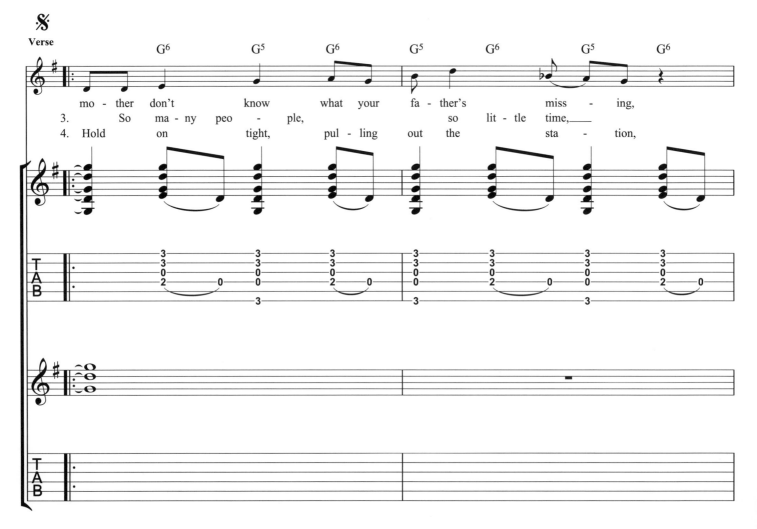

Verse

mo - ther   don't   know   what your   fa - ther's   miss - ing,

3.   So ma - ny peo - ple,   so   lit - tle   time,__

4. Hold   on   tight,   pul - ling   out   the   sta - tion,

Stand-ing on the edge of the noise.___ Stand-ing on the edge of the noise.__

Stand - ing on the edge of the noise.____

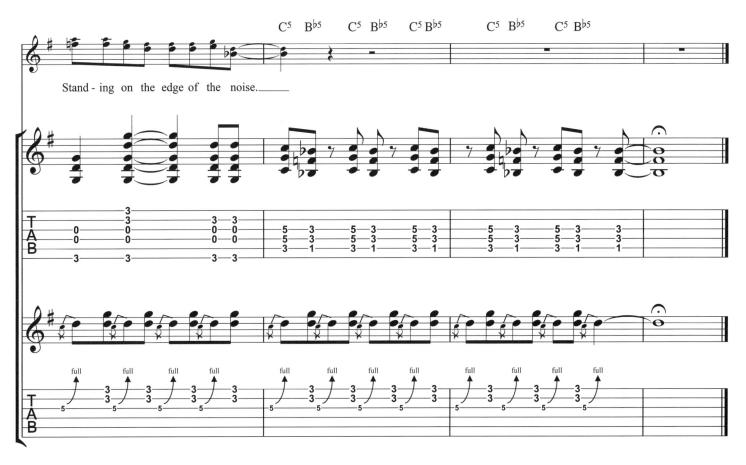

Stand - ing on the edge of the noise.____

WIGWAM

Words & Music by Liam Gallagher, Gem Archer & Andy Bell

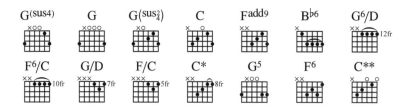

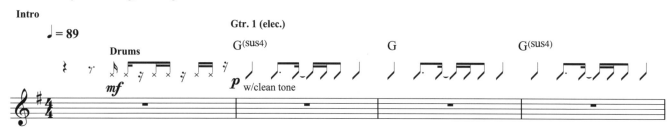

To match original recording, tune all guitars down one semitone

Intro

Verse

1. The chips are down, you're in a- gain,
win or lose, you feel the same. An- oth - er bot - tle in the hand,

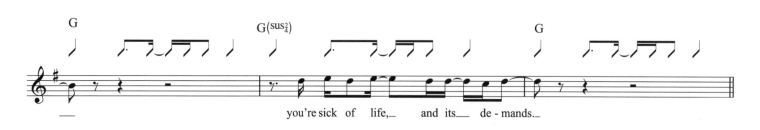

you're sick of life, and its de - mands.

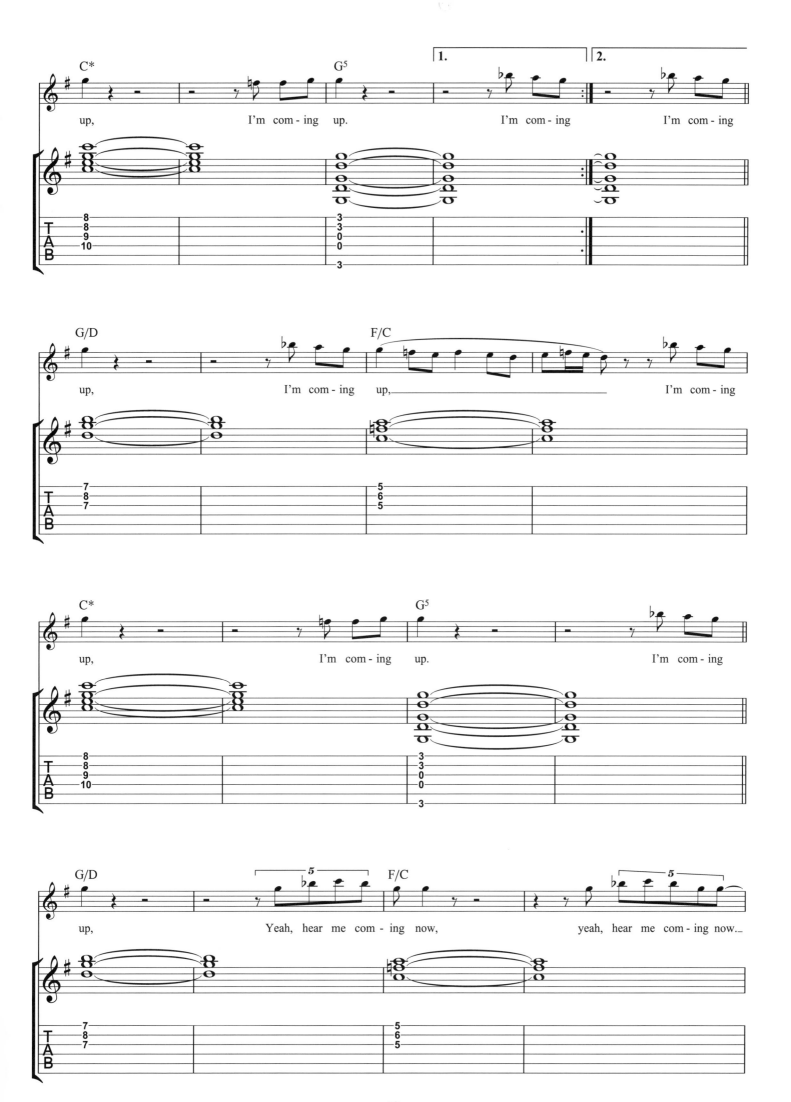

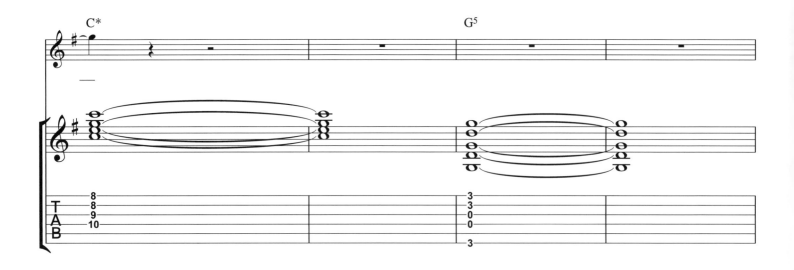

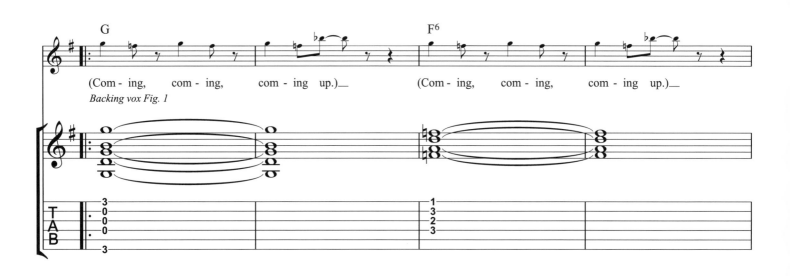

(Com - ing, com - ing, com - ing up.)___ (Com - ing, com - ing, com - ing up.)___

Backing vox Fig. 1

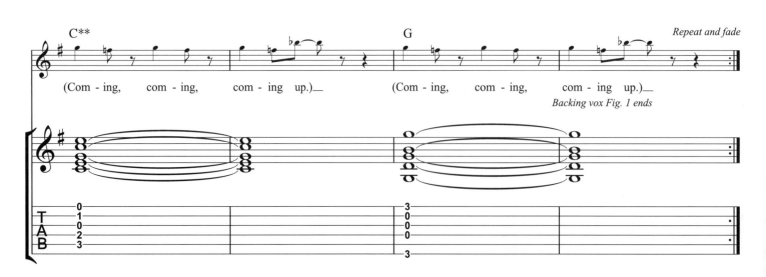

(Com - ing, com - ing, com - ing up.)___ (Com - ing, com - ing, com - ing up.)___

Backing vox Fig. 1 ends

THREE RING CIRCUS

Words & Music by Liam Gallagher, Gem Archer & Andy Bell

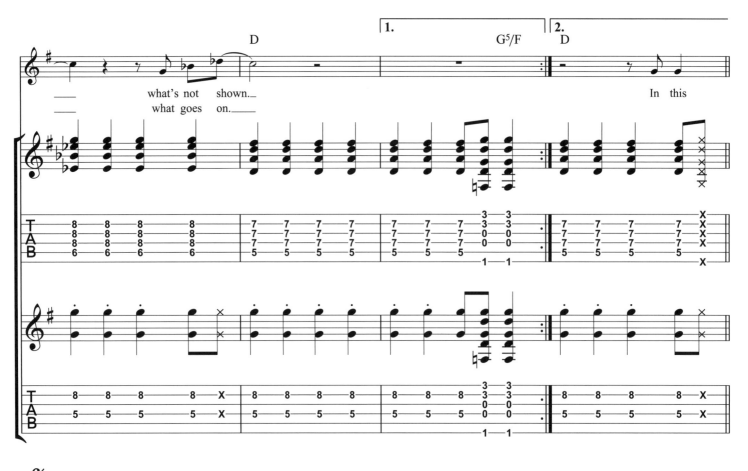

Chorus

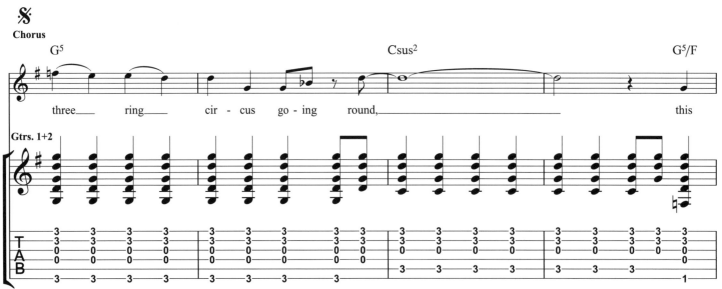

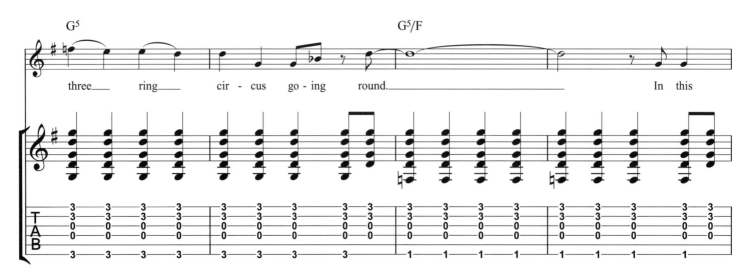

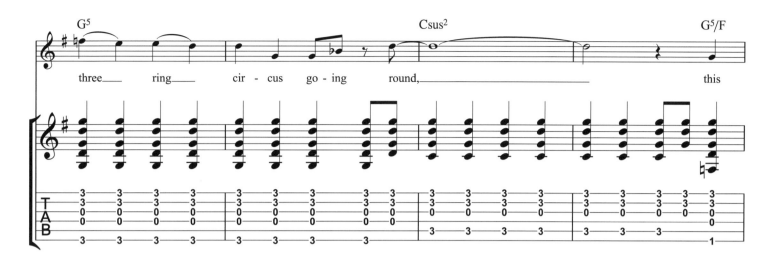

three___ ring___ cir - cus go - ing round,_____ this

To Coda ⊕

three___ ring___ cir - cus go - ing round._____

Solo

Gtr. 3 (elec.)

Gtr. 3 w/dist.
Gtrs. 1+2 play Fig. 1

*Backwards guitar

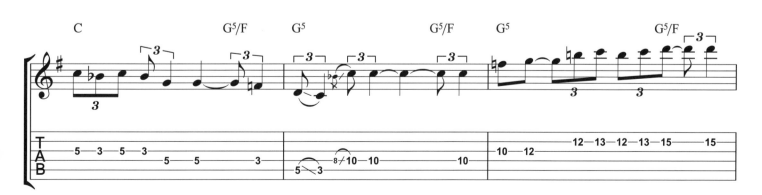

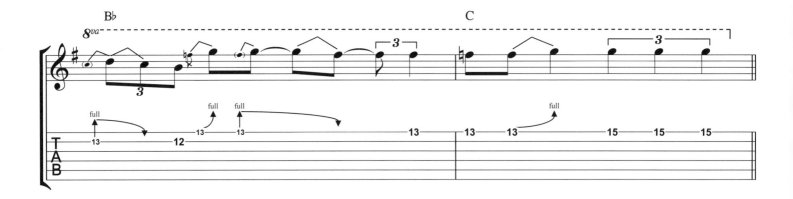

Bridge

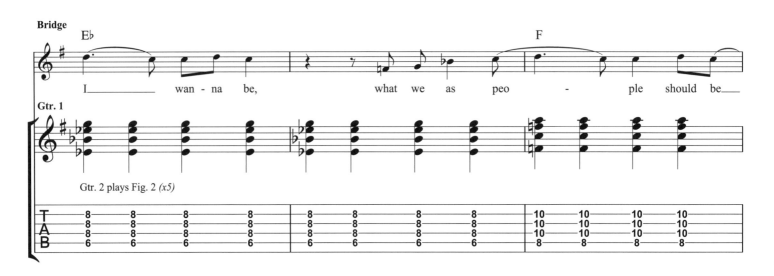

I_____ wan - na be, what we as peo - ple should be___

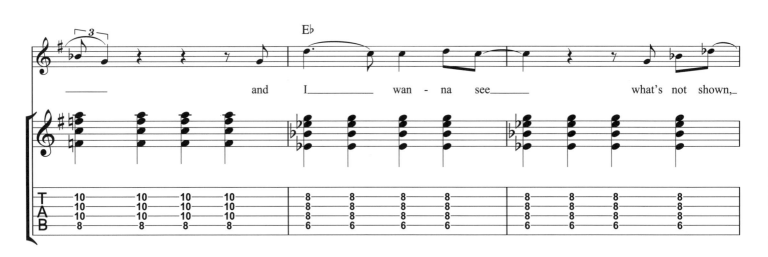

___ and I_____ wan - na see_____ what's not shown,_

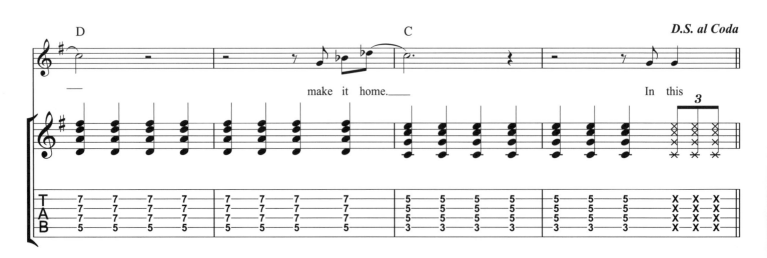

__ make it home.___ In this

74

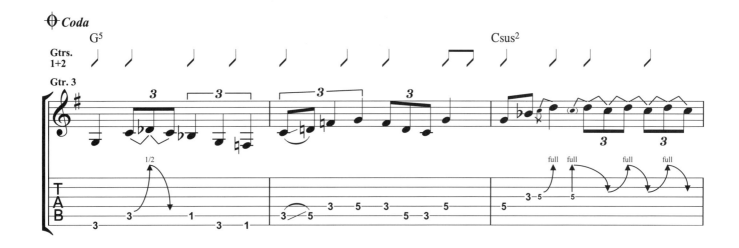

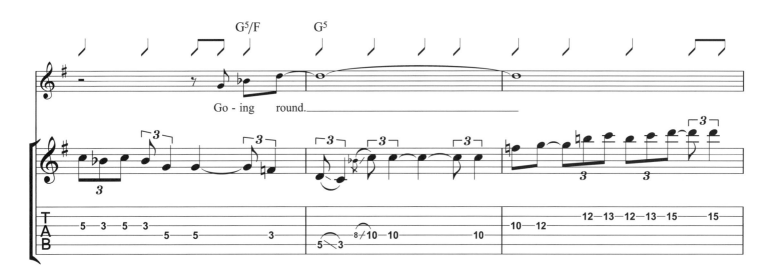

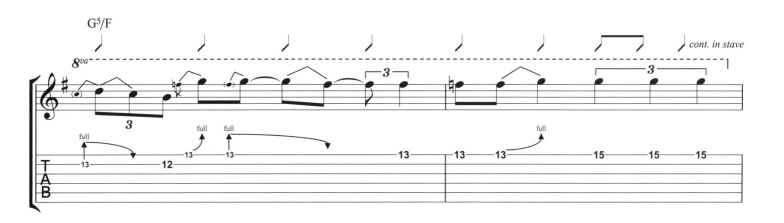

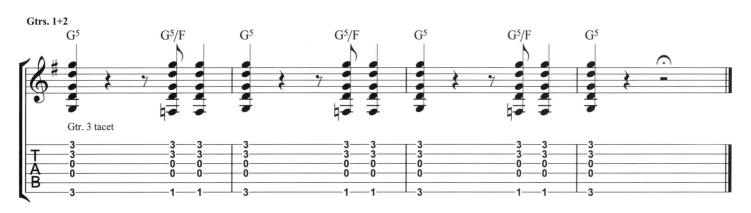

THE BEAT GOES ON

Words & Music by Liam Gallagher, Gem Archer & Andy Bell

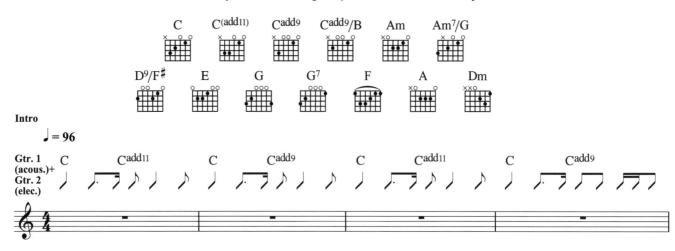

1. Thought that I'd died___ to - day,___ walked off the stage,___ fa - ded a - way___
2. Thought I'd know just what to do,___ that it - 'd be,___ how I want - ed it to.___

___ up through the clouds.___ To 'the gig in the sky'.___ And when I ar - rived,___
___ The Ox and Moon___ were count - ing me in,___ I had to give in,___

the an - gels were sing - ing this song,___ yeah, you know the one,___
make the thun - der and light - ning sing. In the eye of the storm,

___ are you sing - ing a - long?___
___ there's no right and no wrong.

Chorus

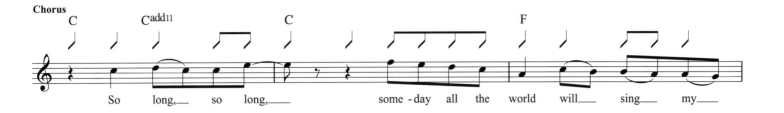

So long,— so long,— some-day all the world will— sing— my—

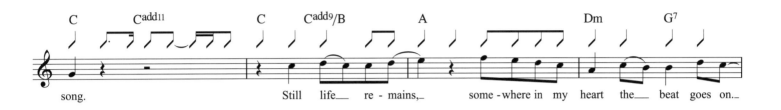

song. Still life— re-mains,— some-where in my heart the— beat goes on.—

—

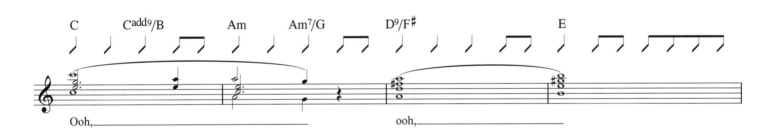

Ooh,— ooh,—

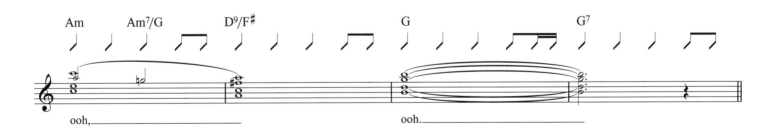

ooh,— ooh.—

Verse

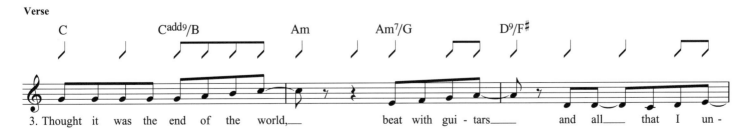

3. Thought it was the end of the world,— beat with gui-tars— and all— that I un-

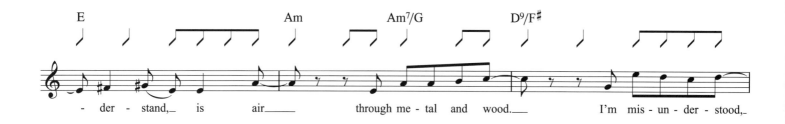

-der - stand,— is air⎯ through me - tal and wood.⎯ I'm mis - un - der - stood,—

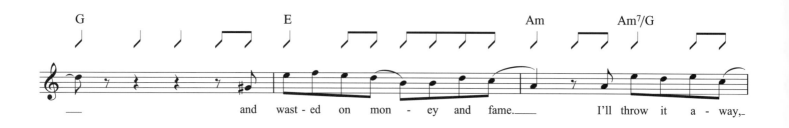

⎯ and wast - ed on mon - ey and fame.⎯ I'll throw it a - way,—

⎯ just to prove that I can.⎯ I'm the last of a dy - ing breed.⎯

⎯ And it's not the end⎯ of the world, oh no,⎯ it's not ev - en the end⎯ of the day.

Chorus

So long,— so long,⎯ some - day all the world will⎯ sing⎯ my⎯ song.

1, 2.

Still life⎯ re - mains,⎯ some - where in my heart the⎯ beat goes on.⎯

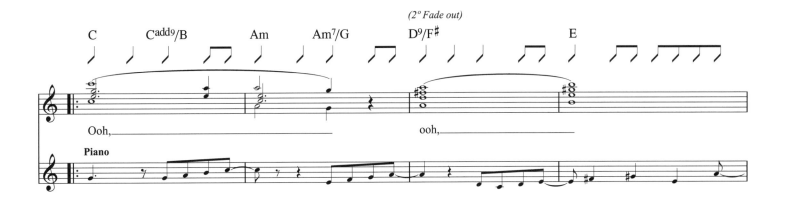

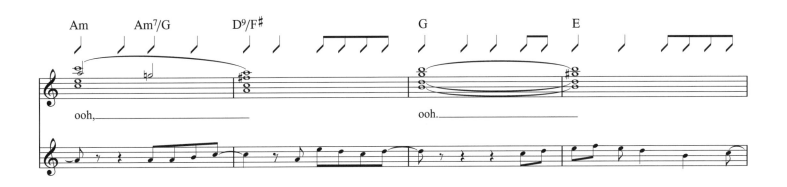

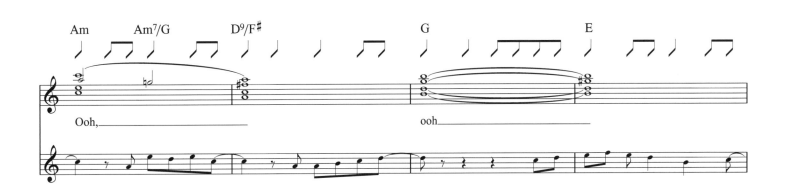

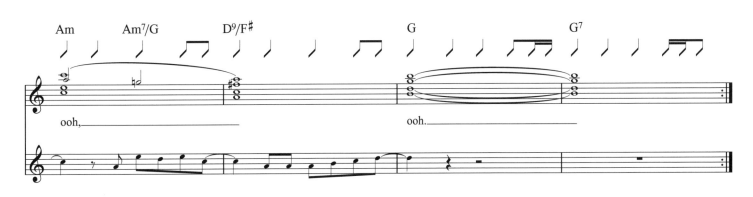

THE MORNING SON

Words & Music by Liam Gallagher, Gem Archer & Andy Bell

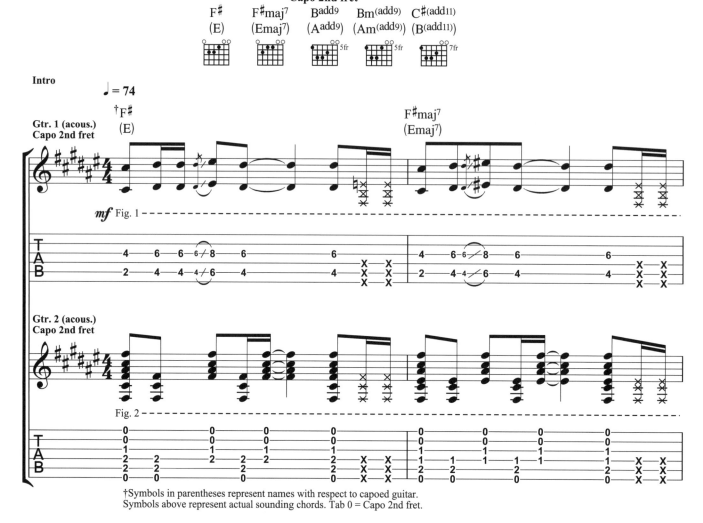

†Symbols in parentheses represent names with respect to capoed guitar.
Symbols above represent actual sounding chords. Tab 0 = Capo 2nd fret.

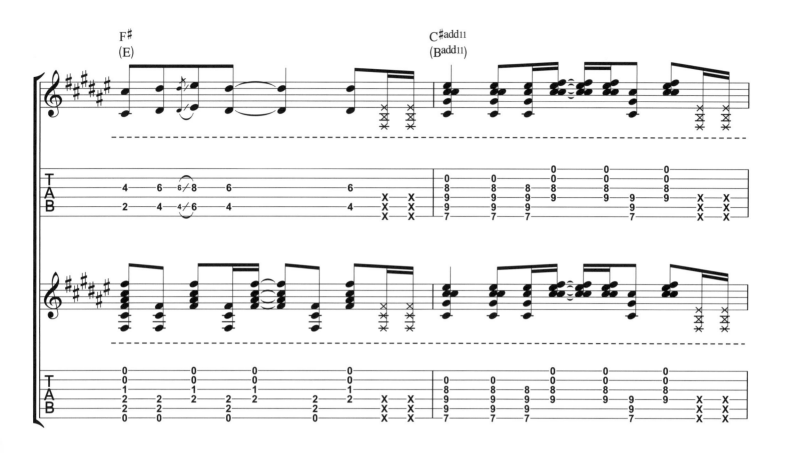

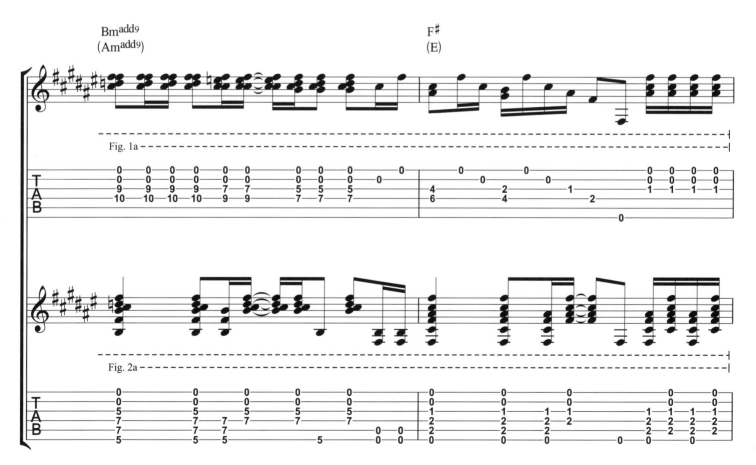